IT SEEMS THAT VERY FEW PEOPLE FEEL THEIR BEST FIRST THING IN THE MORNING —

IN MOST HOUSEHOLDS BREAKFAST IS THE QUIETEST MEAL OF THE DAY

© 1987
Barry Appleby

3904

THE OCCASIONAL VISITS BY OUR NEICE AND NEPHEW CERTAINLY LIVEN UP OUR LIVES AND MAKE US FEEL QUITE YOUNG AGAIN

We were criticised for this cartoon by one reader who complained that it was teaching children to cheat and setting a bad example to others. We replied that we didn't think that children needed any teaching.

This cartoon brought us literally hundreds of letters from readers complaining that George and Gaye would have been LATE for the Church Service not two hours early. Many people insisted that the Gambols were right. Readers drew up diagrams to prove their point. There were arguments in offices, shops, factories and homes. In fact everywhere that people gathered. One poor husband was called a chauvinistic pig for altering the clock in the first place. What do you think?

GAYE STILL PREFERS
THE OLD-FASHIONED
CALCULATOR

A CAR HAS BECOME AN ABSOLUTELY ESSENTIAL PART
OF OUR LIVES—WE JUST DON'T KNOW HOW WE MANAGED
WITHOUT ONE—FORTUNATELY HOWEVER GAYE
HAS BECOME VERY MECHANICALLY MINDED

THE GAMBOLS HAVE SO MANY FRIENDS THAT WHEN THEY GIVE A PARTY THE PROBLEM IS WHO TO LEAVE OUT OF THE GUEST LIST

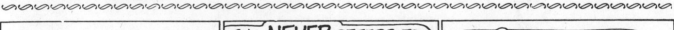

GAYE TAKES A GREAT PRIDE IN HER APPEARANCE NOT ONLY FOR HER OWN SAKE BUT TO PLEASE GEORGE

NO DEAR - NOT TODAY - IT'S FRIDAY

FRIDAY'S THE DAY YOU'RE ALL PRACTICAL AND MUCK IN WITH THE DECORATING

SATURDAY NIGHT'S THE TIME YOU'RE DEMURE AND HELPLESS

©1988 Barry Appleby

4-098

IT DIDN'T TAKE GAYE LONG TO GET THE
OFFICE ORGANIZED TO HER WAYS

The funny thing about office computers and word processors is the ease with which even the youngest of the typists accept them into their working lives with no trouble at all.

D-I-Y — EVERYBODY'S DOING IT THESE DAYS —
IT ALL LOOKS SO EASY

THE TROUBLE WITH HAVING A LOFT IS THAT YOU TEND TO STORE ALL THOSE OLD SOUVENIRS, OLD WORN OUT TREASURES AND EVERYTHING THAT YOU JUST CAN'T BRING YOURSELF TO THROW AWAY

IT'S STUPID TO BE SENTIMENTAL ABOUT THIS OLD RUBBISH

NOW WHAT DO WE DO WITH IT?

THIS WAS A WEDDING PRESENT

28-6

HOLIDAYS —
IF ONLY LIFE WERE AS CAREFREE ALL THE TIME

EVERY TIME OUR NEPHEW AND NEICE
COME TO STAY WITH US WE LEARN
SOMETHING NEW

BANG BANG BANG

I THOUGHT IT WAS YOU— I RECOGNISED YOUR KNOCK

© 1987 Barry Appleby

40
65

© 1988 Barry Appleby

NEVER MIND 'WHY NOT?'

10-1

ONE SHOP SELLS BETTER GOODS THAN ANOTHER ONE IS CHEAPER BUT THE OTHER IS NEARER AND YET ANOTHER HAS A BIGGER CAR PARK— SHOPPING'S A VERY COMPLICATED JOB THESE DAYS

4038

CAN YOU SEE ANYTHING WRONG WITH THIS CARTOON?— LOTS OF PEOPLE WROTE TO POINT OUT THAT GAYE WAS ASKING TO HAVE HER HANDBAG STOLEN BY PUTTING IT ON THE FLOOR BY HER FEET

GEORGE IS A GREAT SPORTSMAN..ER..BUT NOT OF THE ACTIVE KIND

HERE WE ARE

DERBY RUNNERS - RIDERS

ALL THE INFORMATION YOU NEED TO FIND THE WINNER

NO DEAR - IT DOESN'T TELL YOU THE COLOUR OF THE JOCKEY'S EYES

DERBY RUNNERS RIDERS OWNERS TRAINERS FORM

AND I ONLY BACK HORSES RIDDEN BY JOCKEYS WITH BROWN EYES

DERBY RUNNERS RIDERS OWNERS TRAINERS FORM

© 1987 Barry Appleby

3888

Most people worry about their weight AFTER Christmas – but not the Gambols. They know that it's just impossible to avoid over-eating and drinking at this time of the year. So Gaye insists that they get their weight down BEFORE Christmas. Well – It sounds logical.

GAYE SPENDS WEEKS PLANNING THE FOOD FOR CHRISTMAS—
HOURS COOKING IT AND THEN GRUMBLES WHEN GEORGE
EATS AND PUTS ON WEIGHT

AND SO WE COME TO THE END OF YET ANOTHER SELECTION OF OUR CARTOONS — BUT DON'T FORGET THAT THERE WILL BE MORE IN THE DAILY EXPRESS AND SUNDAY EXPRESS AND IN MANY NEWSPAPERS OUTSIDE THE UNITED KINGDOM TOMORROW AND EVERY DAY

© 1988 Barry Appleby

Published by Express Newspapers plc, Fleet Street, London EC4P 4JT, and printed by Purnell Book Production Limited. Member of BPCC plc